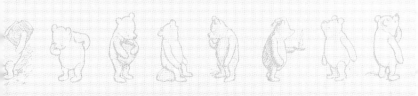

THE
PROVERBIAL
POOH

Wise words from
Winnie-the-Pooh

EGMONT

First published in Great Britain 2002
by Egmont Books Limited
239 Kensington High Street, London, W8 6SA

ISBN 1 4052 0105 3

Printed in Singapore

Edward Bear, known to his friends as Winnie-the-Pooh, or Pooh, knows that it's sometimes hard to say what you mean. With these wise sayings on food, friendship, bravery and wisdom, you'll never be lost for the perfect proverb.

FOOD

'just a mouthful
of condensed milk or
whatnot, with perhaps
a lick of honey —'

'I just like to know,' said Pooh humbly. 'So as I can say to myself: "I've got fourteen pots of honey left." Or fifteen, as the case may be. It's sort of comforting.'

'I think,' said Christopher Robin, 'that we ought to eat all our Provisions now, so that we shan't have so much to carry.'

'And the only
reason for being
a bee that
I know of is
making honey.'

'And the only reason
for making honey
is so as I can eat it.'

'You never can tell
with bees.'

'It all comes, I suppose...
it all comes of liking
honey so much.'

'It all comes,' said Pooh crossly,
'of not having front doors
big enough.'

'It all comes,'
said Rabbit sternly, 'of eating too much.'

'How long does getting thin take?'
asked Pooh anxiously.

'About a week, I should think.'

The more he shook it,
the more tightly it stuck.

'If a bottle can float,
then a jar can float,
and if a jar floats,
I can sit on the top of it,
if it's a very big jar.'

'I remember my uncle saying once
that he had seen cheese
just this colour.'

'Nearly eleven o'clock,'
said Pooh happily.
'You're just in time
for a little
smackerel of
something.'

... although Eating Honey was a very good thing to do, there was a moment just before you began to eat it which was better than when you were, but he didn't know what it was called.

'Well,' said Pooh,
'if I plant
a honeycomb
outside my
house, then
it will grow up
into a beehive.'

... every Heffalump
... was making
straight for a pot
of Pooh's honey,
and eating it all.

'When you wake up in the morning, Pooh,' said Piglet at last, 'what's the first thing you say to yourself?'

'What's for breakfast?' said Pooh. 'What do you say, Piglet?'

'I say, I wonder what's going to happen exciting to-day?' said Piglet.

Pooh nodded thoughtfully.
'It's the same thing,' he said.

FRIENDSHIP

I could spend a happy morning
Seeing Piglet.
And I couldn't spend
a happy morning
Not seeing Piglet.

. . . he gave a very long sigh and said, 'I wish Pooh were here. It's so much more friendly with two.'

'Mind you don't get blown away, little Piglet. You'd be missed.'

'If I know anything about anything,
that hole means Rabbit,' he said,
'and Rabbit means Company,' he said,
'and Company means Food and
Listening-to-Me-Humming and such like.'

'... last week or the week before
... Rabbit bumped into me and
said "Bother!" The Social Round.
Always something going on.'

'Sad? Why should I be sad? It's my birthday. The happiest day of the year.'

'Nobody can be
uncheered with a balloon.'

... he said, 'Silly old Bear,' in such a loving voice that everybody felt quite hopeful again.

'...every time I want to sit
down for a little rest, I have
to brush away half a dozen
of Rabbit's smaller
friends-and-relations first...'

'...it's always useful to know where a friend-or-relation is, whether you want him or whether you don't.'

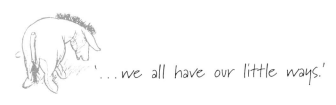 '…we all have our little ways.'

'I haven't seen Roo for
a long time, and if I don't
see him to-day it will be
a still longer time.'

... really, it wasn't much good having anything exciting like floods, if you couldn't share them with somebody.

'...it is well known that if One of the Fiercer Animals is Deprived of Its Young, it becomes as fierce as Two of the Fiercer Animals.'

'A little Consideration, a little Thought
for Others, makes all the difference.'

...how sad it was to be an Animal
who had never had a bunch
of violets picked for him.

'Here I am,' said a
growly voice behind him.
'Pooh!'
They rushed into each
other's arms.

'...when you've been walking in the wind for miles, and you suddenly go into somebody's house, and he says, "Hallo, Pooh, you're just in time for a little smackerel of something," and you are, then it's what I call a Friendly Day.'

'Pooh, whatever happens,
you will understand,
won't you?'

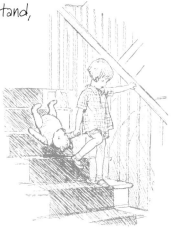

BRAVERY

'It is hard to be brave,'
said Piglet, sniffing slightly,
'when you're only
a Very Small Animal.'

'What?' said Piglet, with a jump. And then, to show that he hadn't been frightened, he jumped up and down once or twice more in an exercising sort of way.

'It's Christopher Robin,' he said.
'Ah, then you'll be all right,' said
Piglet. 'You'll be quite safe with him.'

'We must be practical.'

'Sometimes it is,
and sometimes
it isn't. You never
can tell with
paw-marks.'

Pooh felt that he ought
to say something helpful
about it, but didn't quite
know what. So he
decided to do something
helpful instead.

Then Piglet saw what
a Foolish Piglet he had
been, and he was so ashamed
of himself that he ran
straight off home and went
to bed with a headache.

'If people jump out at you suddenly, that's an Ambush,' said Owl.

'... one must be able to Breathe.'

Owl was explaining that in a case of Sudden and Temporary Immersion the Important Thing was to keep the Head Above Water.

'I don't hold with all this washing,'
grumbled Eeyore. 'This modern
Behind-the-ears nonsense.'

'It's a little Anxious,' he said to himself, 'to be a Very Small Animal Entirely Surrounded by Water.'

'That's what Jagulars always do,'
said Pooh, much interested. 'They call
"Help! Help!" and then when you look
up, they drop on you.'

'Sometimes it's a Boat, and sometimes it's more of an Accident. It all depends.'
'Depends on what?'
'On whether I'm on the top of it or underneath it.'

... he didn't look round,
because if you look round
and see a Very Fierce Heffalump
looking down at you, sometimes you
forget what you were going to say.

'I thought Tiggers were
smaller than that.'
'Not the big ones,'
said Tigger.

'They're funny things,
Accidents. You never
have them till you're
having them.'

'Ah!' said Rabbit, who never let things come to him, but always went and fetched them.

'If you're standing on the slippery bank
of a river, and somebody BOUNCES
you loudly from behind, you slip.'

...it was a thing
which even a
Very Small Animal
could wake up
in the morning
and be comfortable
about doing.

So Pooh rose and sat down and said
'Thank you,' which is the proper
thing to say when you have
been made a Knight...

Wisdom

'It isn't Brain,' he went on
humbly, '...but it comes
to me sometimes.'

'Of course I'm right,' said Pooh.

'Well, either a tail is
there or it isn't
there. You can't make
a mistake about it...'

'...the middle of the night

...is a good time for going to sleep.'

'We can't all, and some of us don't.
That's all there is to it.'

'Many a bear going out on a warm day like this would never have thought of bringing a little something with him.'

'...my spelling is Wobbly. It's good
spelling but it Wobbles, and the letters
get in the wrong places.'

'One mustn't complain.'

'I wish I could jump
like that,' he thought.
'Some can and some
can't. That's how it is.'

. . . you never know when a bit
of string might be Useful.

'This writing business.
Pencils and what-not.
Over-rated, if you
ask me. Silly stuff.
Nothing in it.'

'We'll go because it's Thursday,' he said.

'It just shows what can be done
by taking a little trouble,' said
Eeyore. 'Do you see, Pooh?
Do you see,
Piglet?
Brains first
and then
Hard Work.'

'Being fine to-day doesn't Mean Anything. It has no sig — what's that word? Well, it has none of that.'

'It is the best
way to write
poetry, letting
things come.'

'…Tiggers can't climb
downwards, because their tails
get in the way, only upwards…'

'If there is any thinking to be
done in this Forest — and when
I say thinking I mean *thinking* —
you and I
must do it.'

'It will rain soon, you see
if it doesn't,' he said.

It didn't look at all like a house now; it looked like a tree which had been blown down; and as soon as a house looks like that, it is time you tried to find another one.

'...you can't help respecting anybody
who can spell TUESDAY, even if
he doesn't spell it right...'

'Do you know what A means,
little Piglet?'
'No, Eeyore, I don't.'
'It means Learning, it means Education,
it means all the things that you and Pooh
haven't got. That's what A means.'

'Bouncy or coffy, it's all the same
at the bottom of the river.'

...when you Think of Things, you find sometimes that a Thing which seemed very Thingish inside you is quite different when it gets out into the open and has other people looking at it.

'It's a funny thing,' said Rabbit...
'how everything looks the same in a mist.'

'If anybody wants to clap,'
said Eeyore when he had
read this, 'now is the
time to do it.'